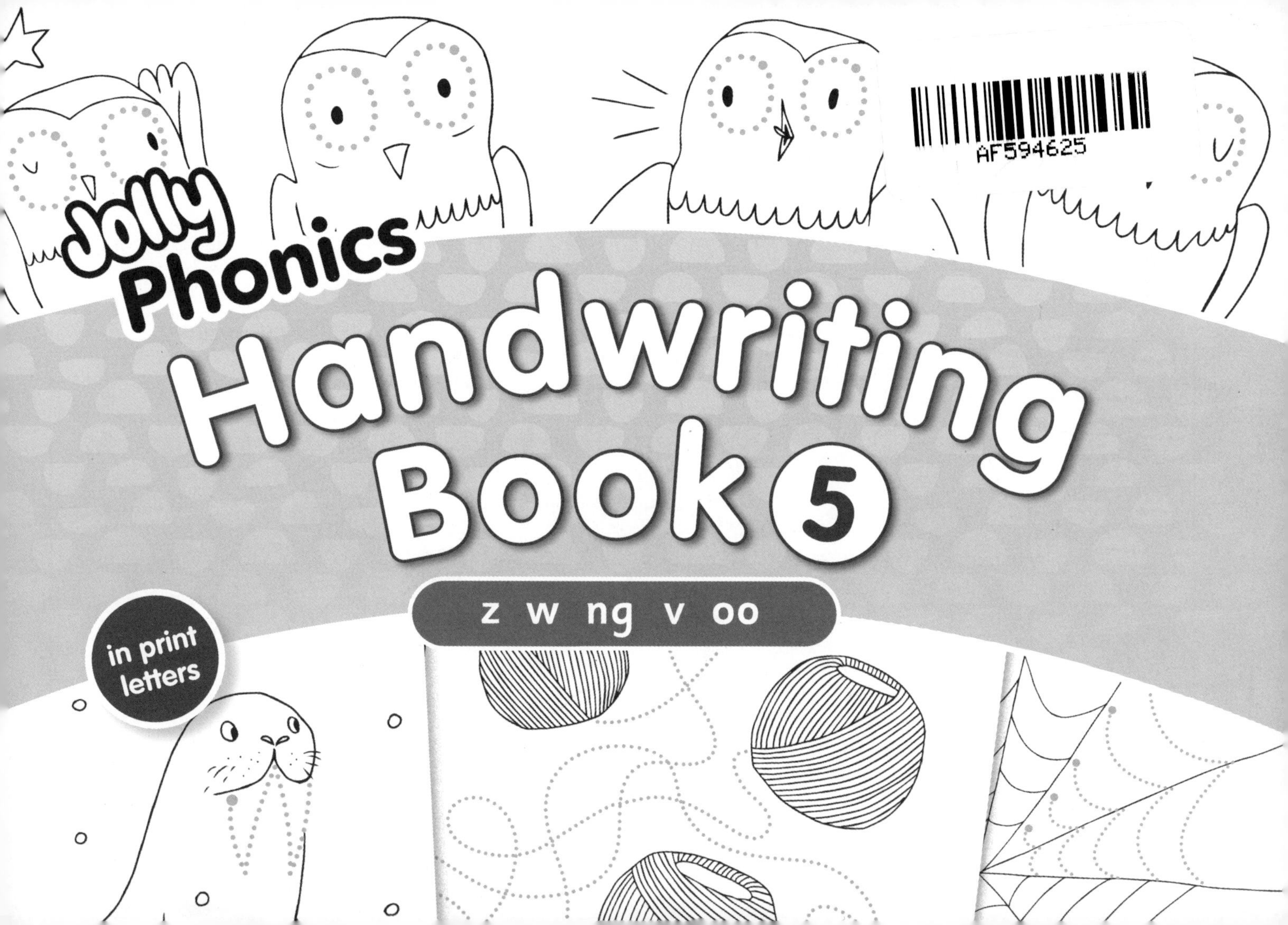

Jolly Phonics
Handwriting Book 5
z w ng v oo
in print letters
AF594625

Guidelines

Good pencil control and correct formation enable students to achieve neat, fluent and, eventually, joined handwriting.

Handwriting practice works best when the students are sitting at their table or desk. This provides a firm flat surface to write on and encourages correct posture.

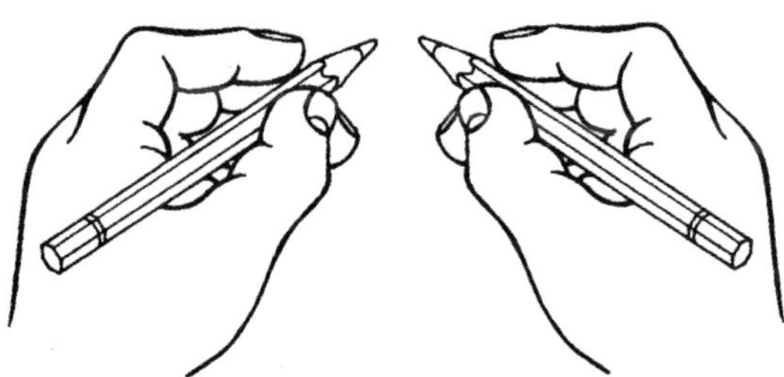

A good pencil hold from the very beginning is extremely important for developing neat, fluent handwriting. The tripod pencil grip is recommended.

Hold the pencil between the thumb and index finger, and support it on the middle finger. As the pencil is moved, the knuckles on the thumb and index finger look like a frog's legs.

Coloring is also a good way to develop fine motor skills. Encourage the students to color carefully, to keep within the lines, and to choose appropriate colors.

Spot the frog

Encourage the students to look out for the frog throughout these books, to remind them to practice their "froggy-leg" grip.

Write your name on the sign and draw your face on the snowman.

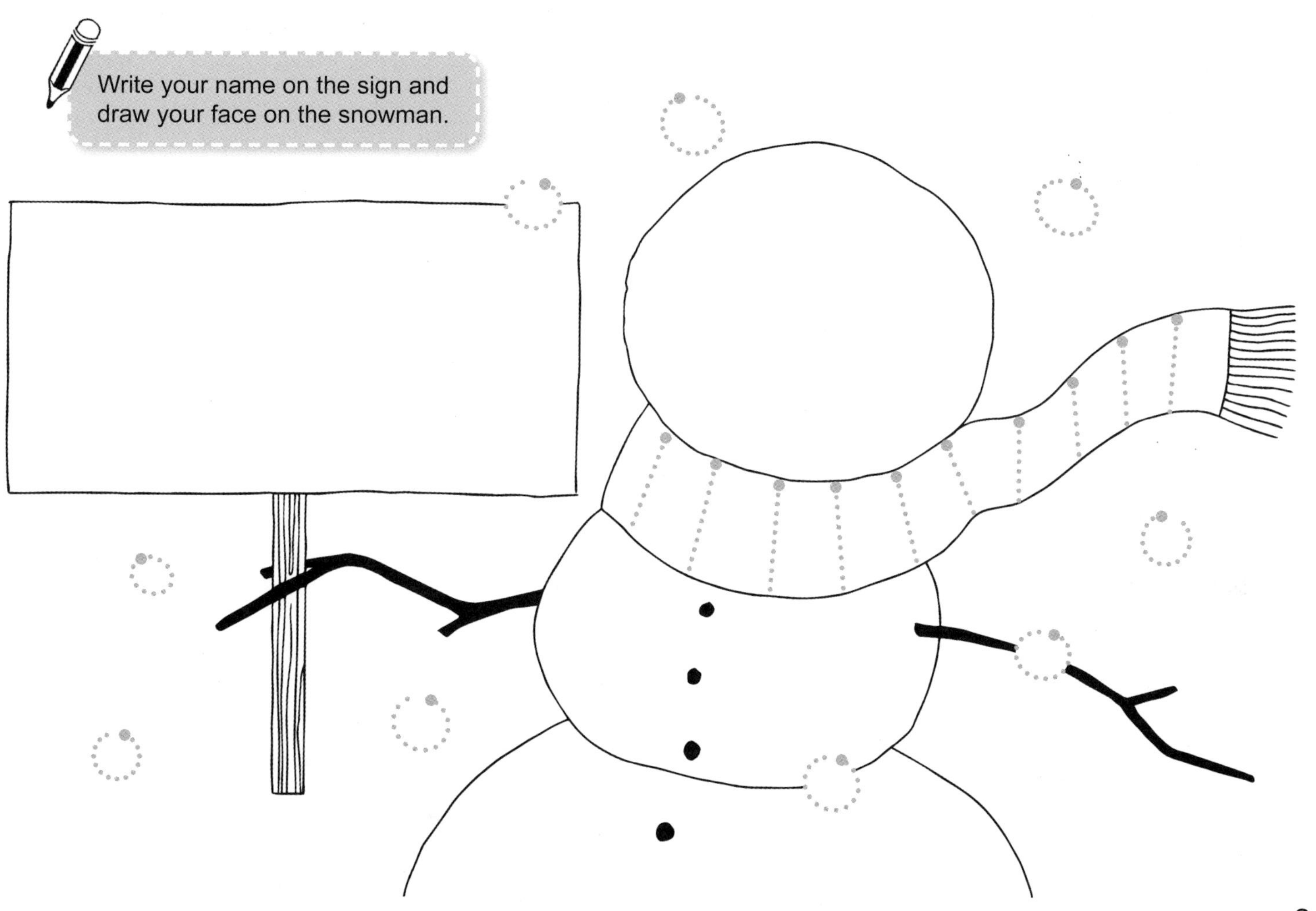

Continue the patterns.

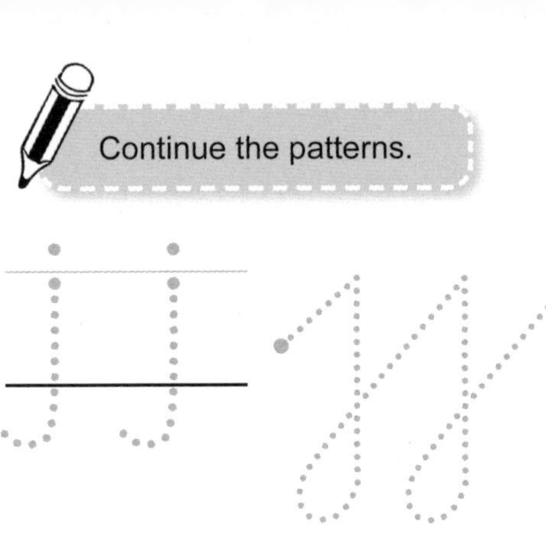

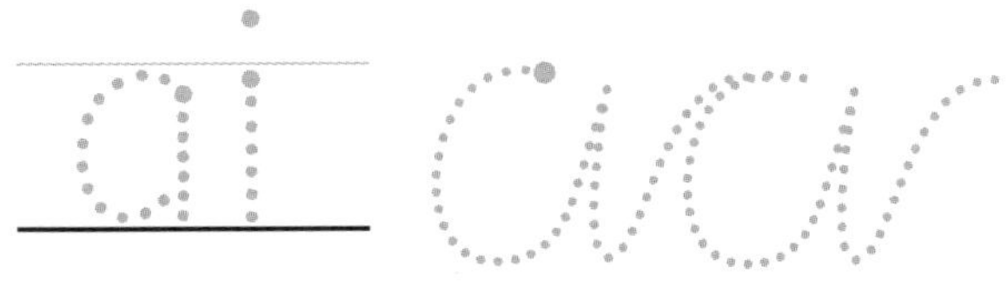

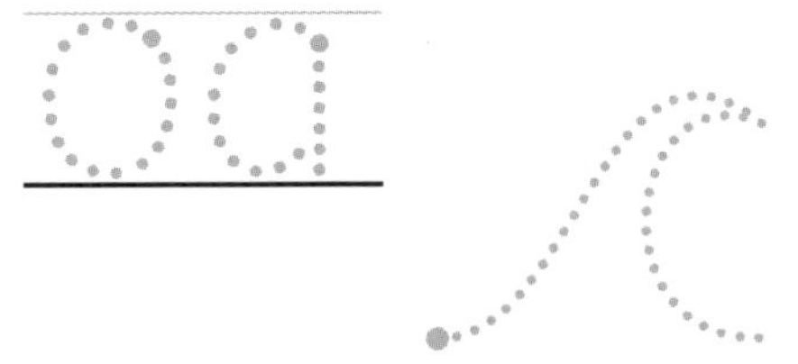

ie

ee

or

Z

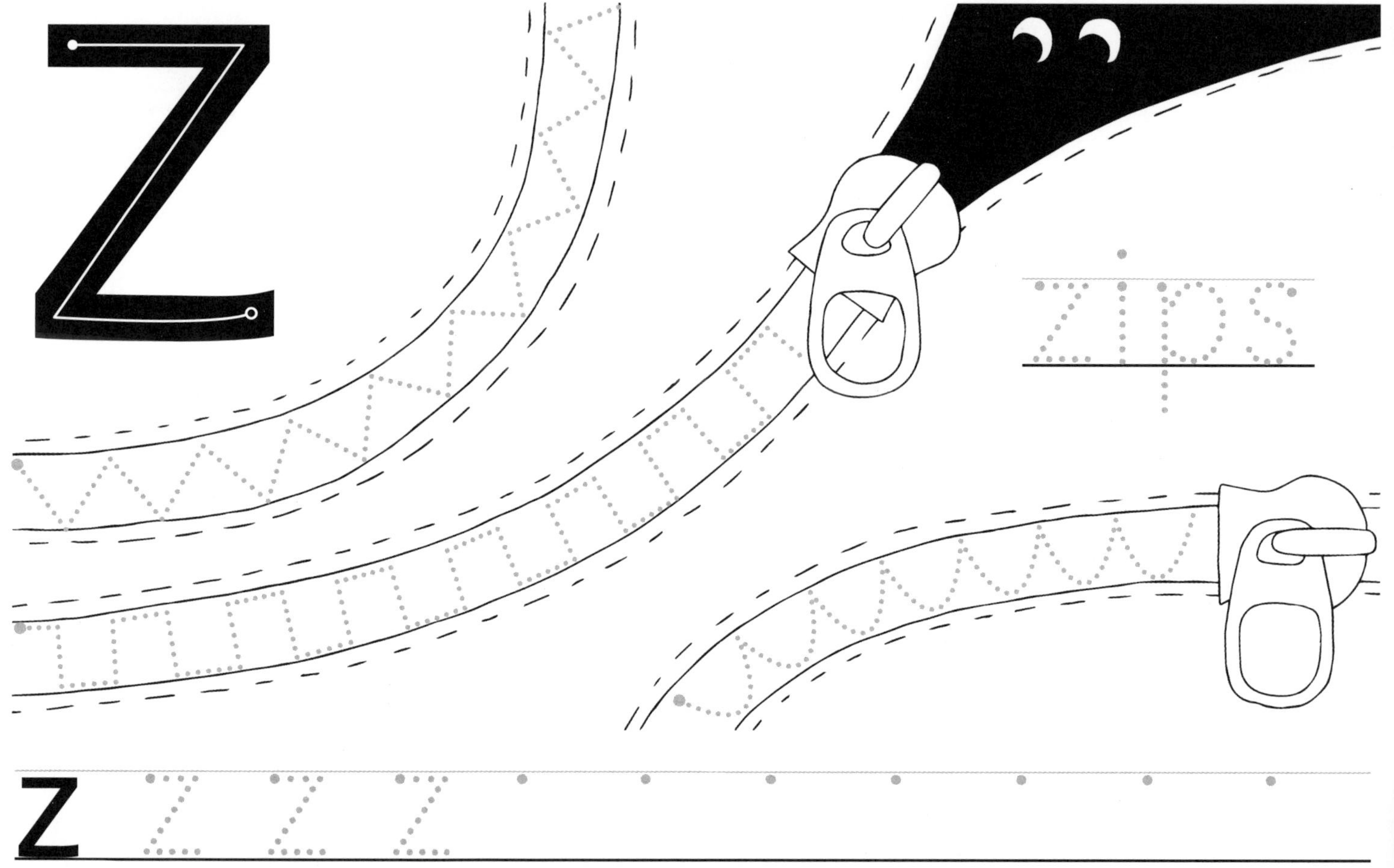

z

Complete the zebras' zigzags.

Can you find two bees in the picture?
What noise do they make?

Why is one walrus watching the wiggly worm?
swim
w

oa ie

The wind has blown holes in the spiderwebs. Can you help mend them?

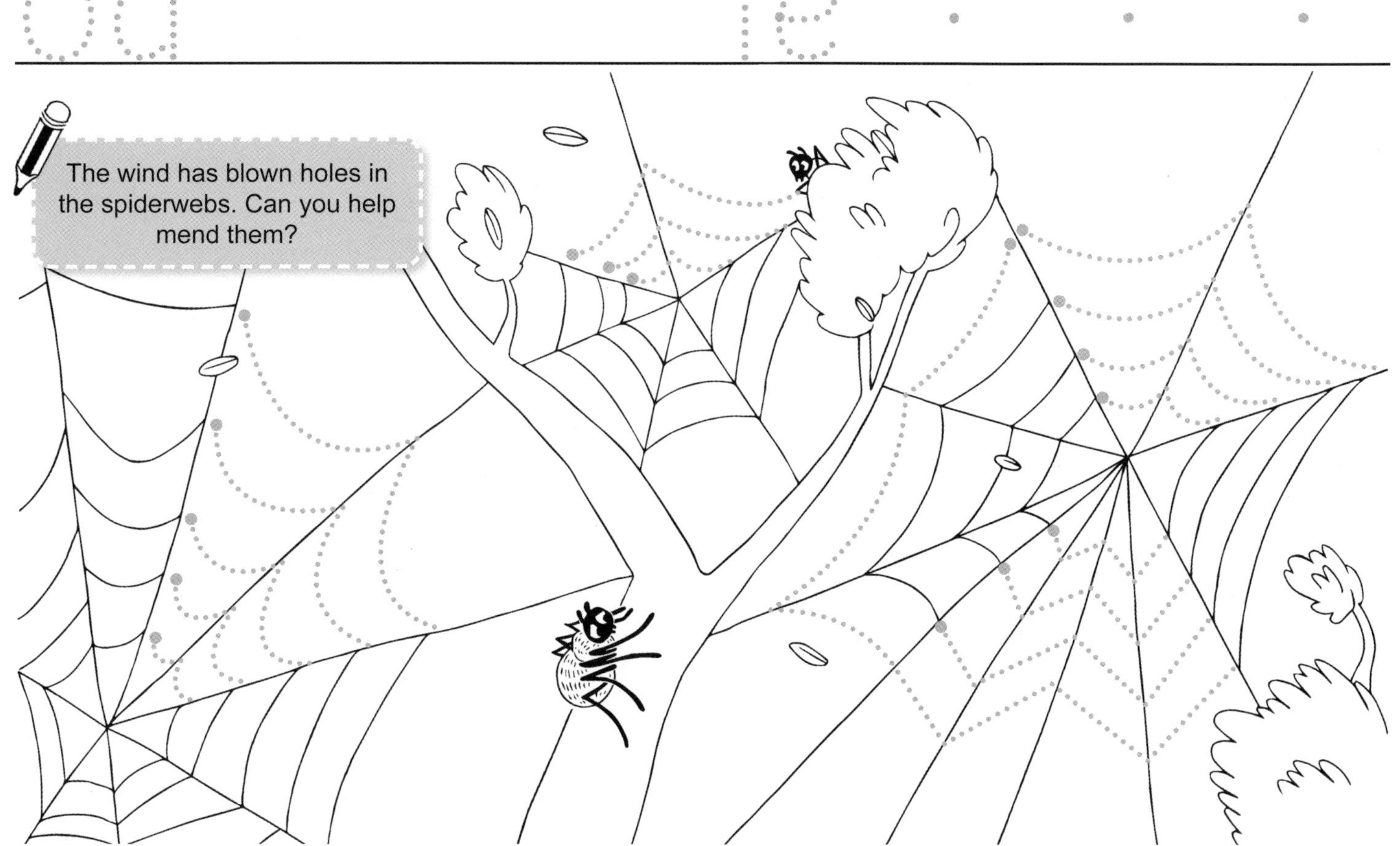

1
2
ng
string
Trace to find out which ball of string the ring is tied to.
ng ng ng

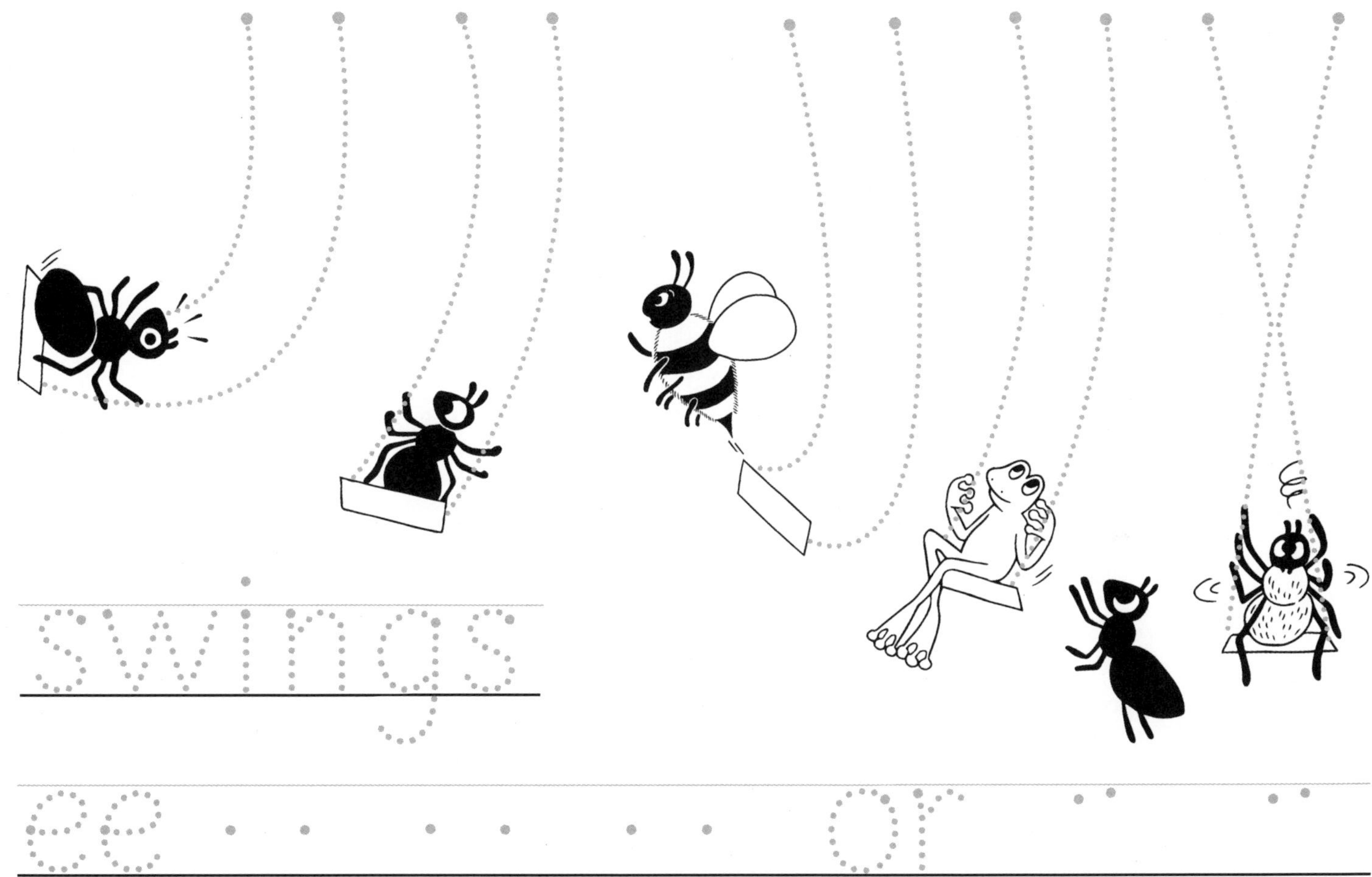

swings

ee . . . . . . or . .

Trace each spring.

swimming training
Why is the ant blowing its whistle?

V
How many flowers can you count?
v

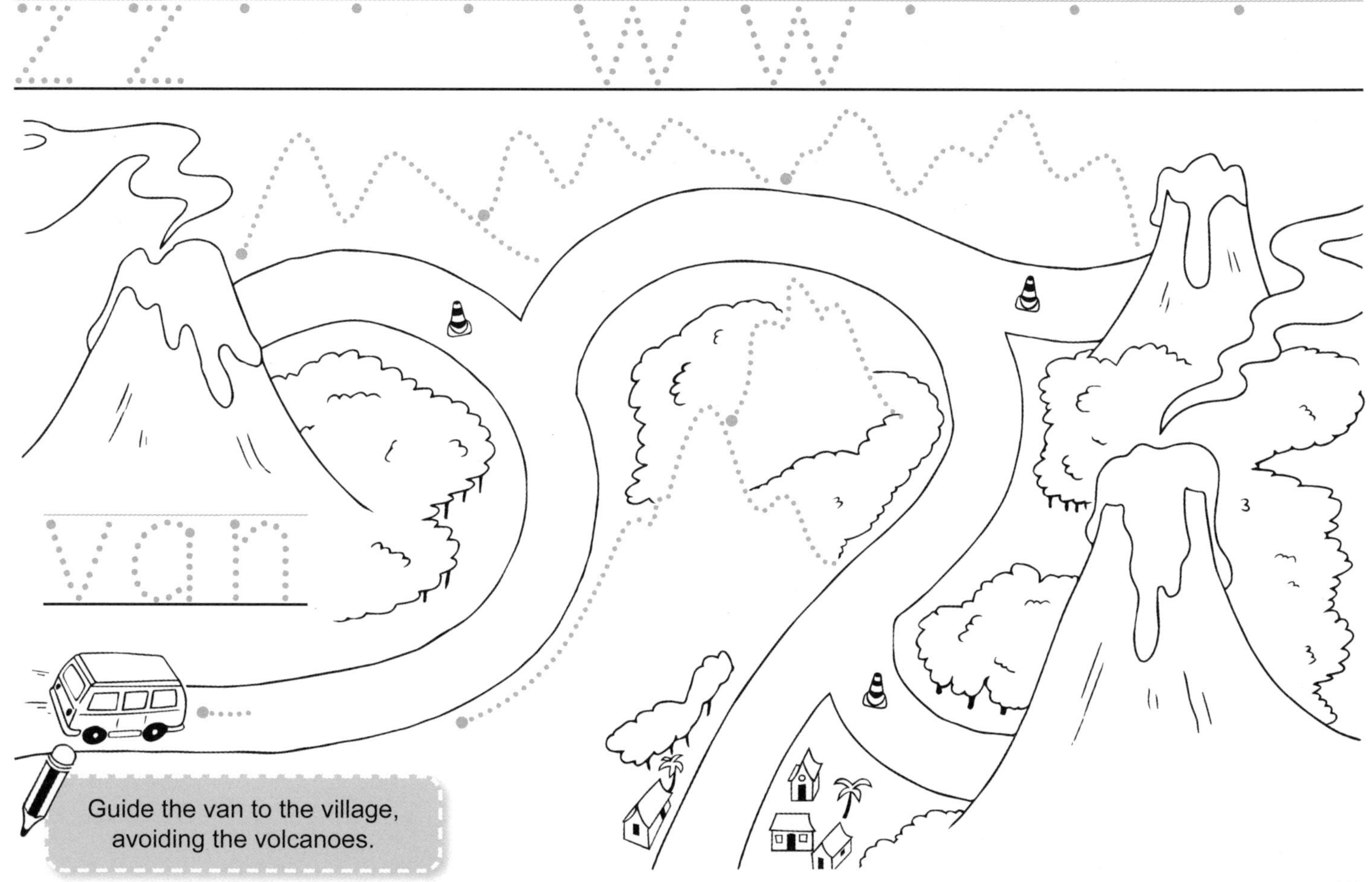

Guide the van to the village, avoiding the volcanoes.

Oo

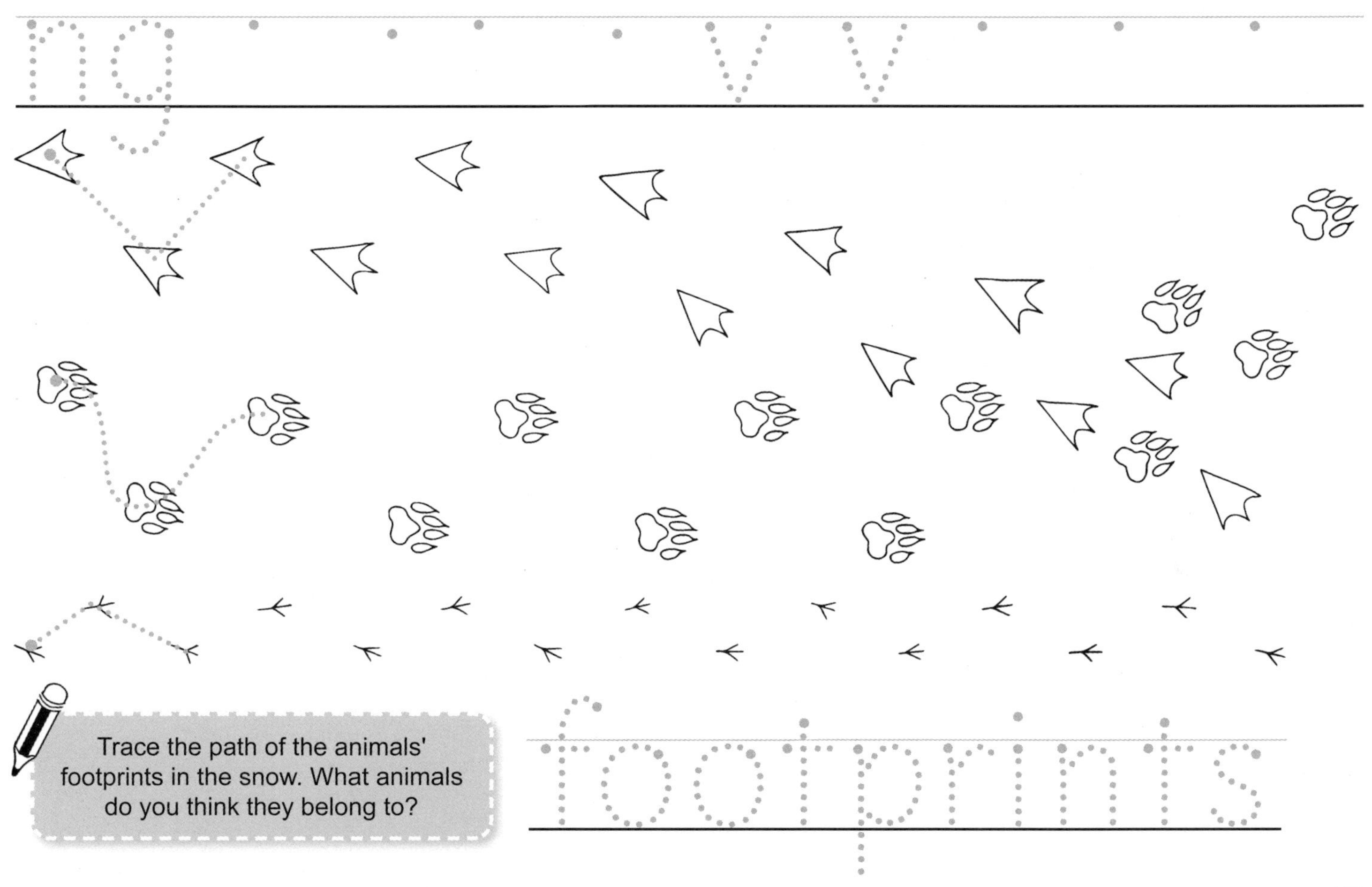

Trace the path of the animals' footprints in the snow. What animals do you think they belong to?

footprints

scrapbook
Have you visited a zoo? What animals did you see?
wombat

Look at the letters on the map and try to think of some animals that begin with those sounds.

Practice writing your digraphs. Can you think of any other words with these sounds in them?

ai ai ai ai

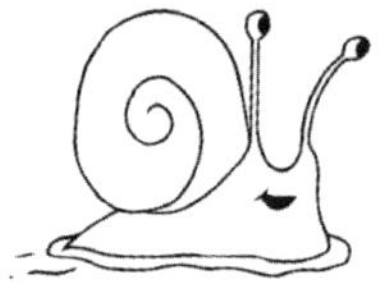

snail

oa oa oa

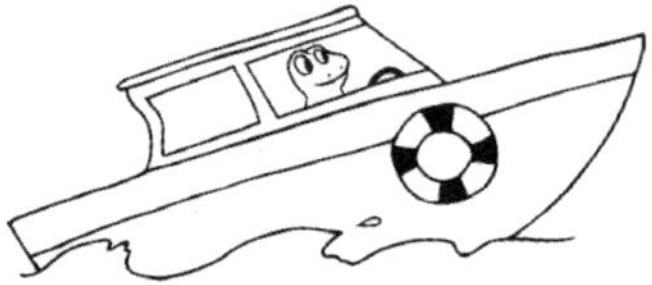

boat

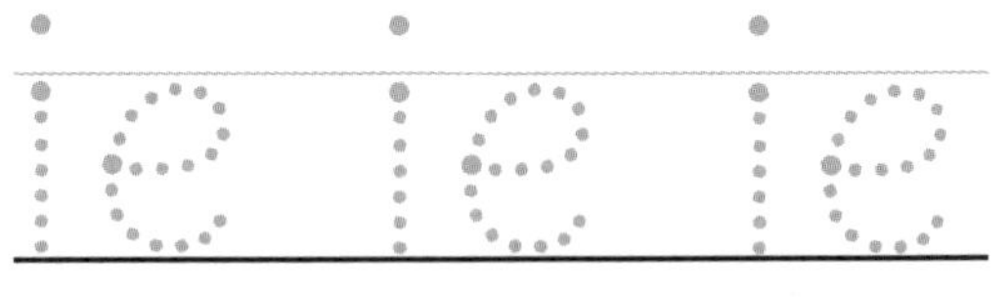

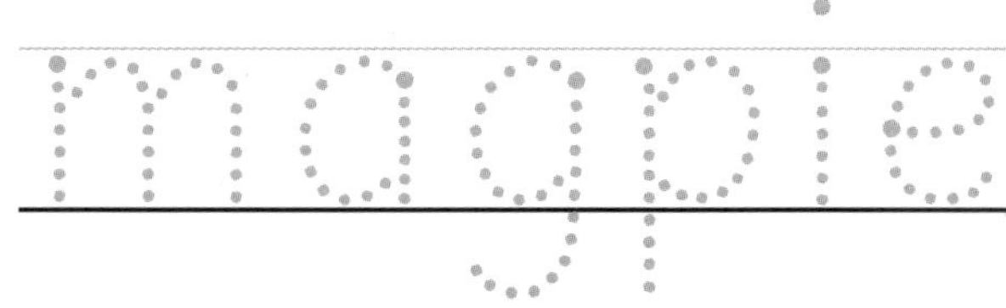

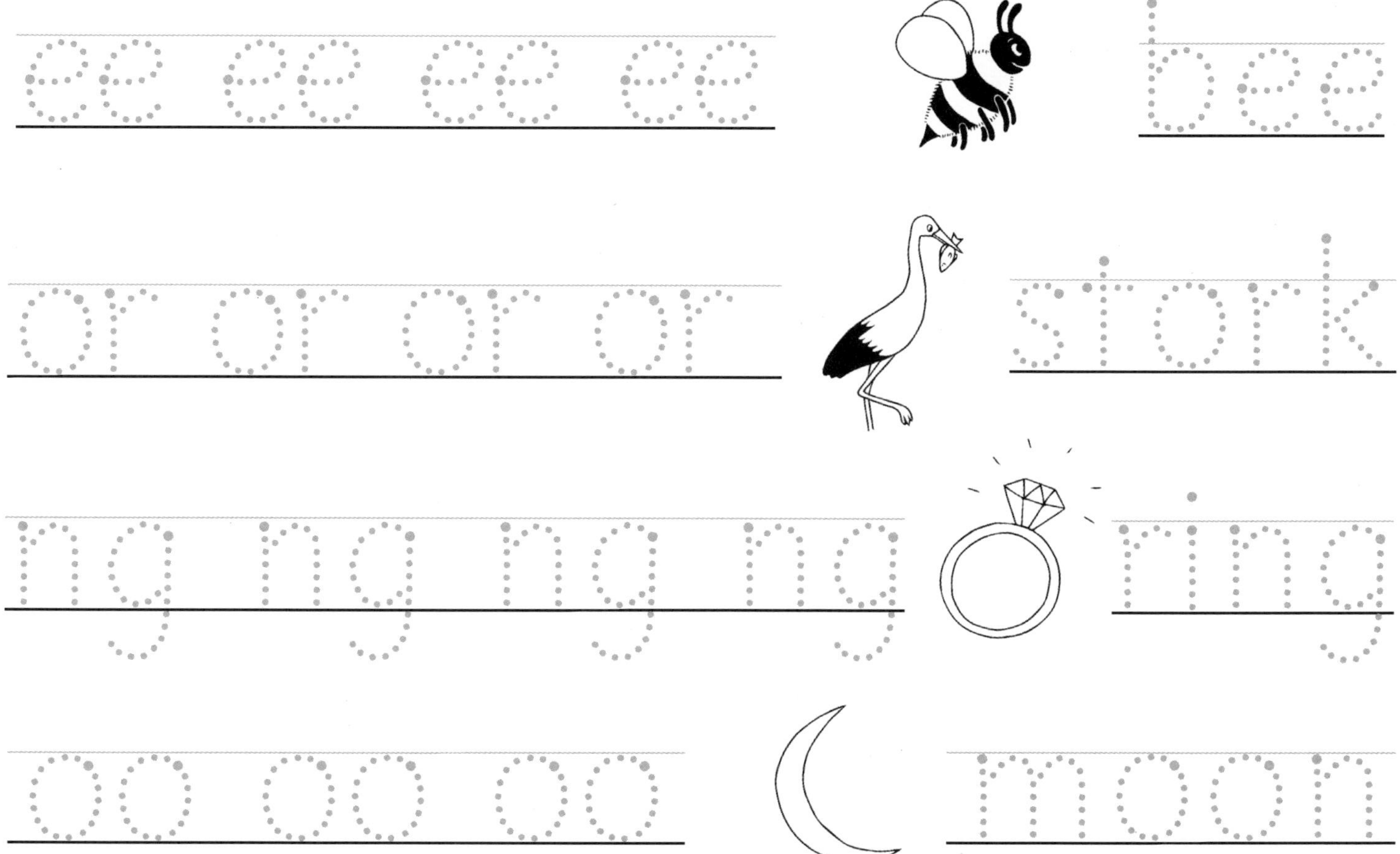

ee ee ee ee
bee
or or or or
stork
ng ng ng ng
ring
oo oo oo
moon

Can you draw something that includes each sound?

z z z

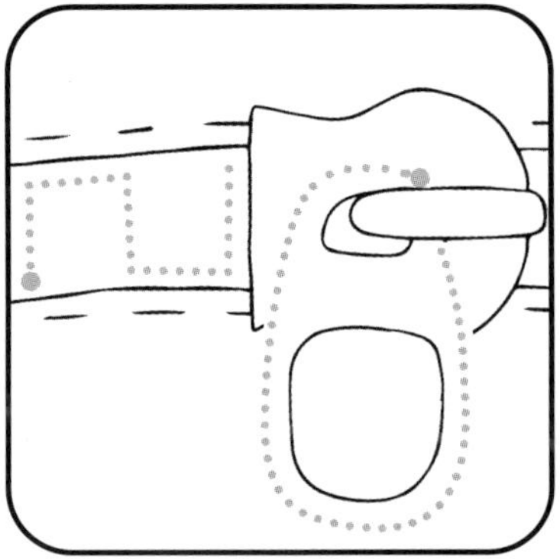

w w w

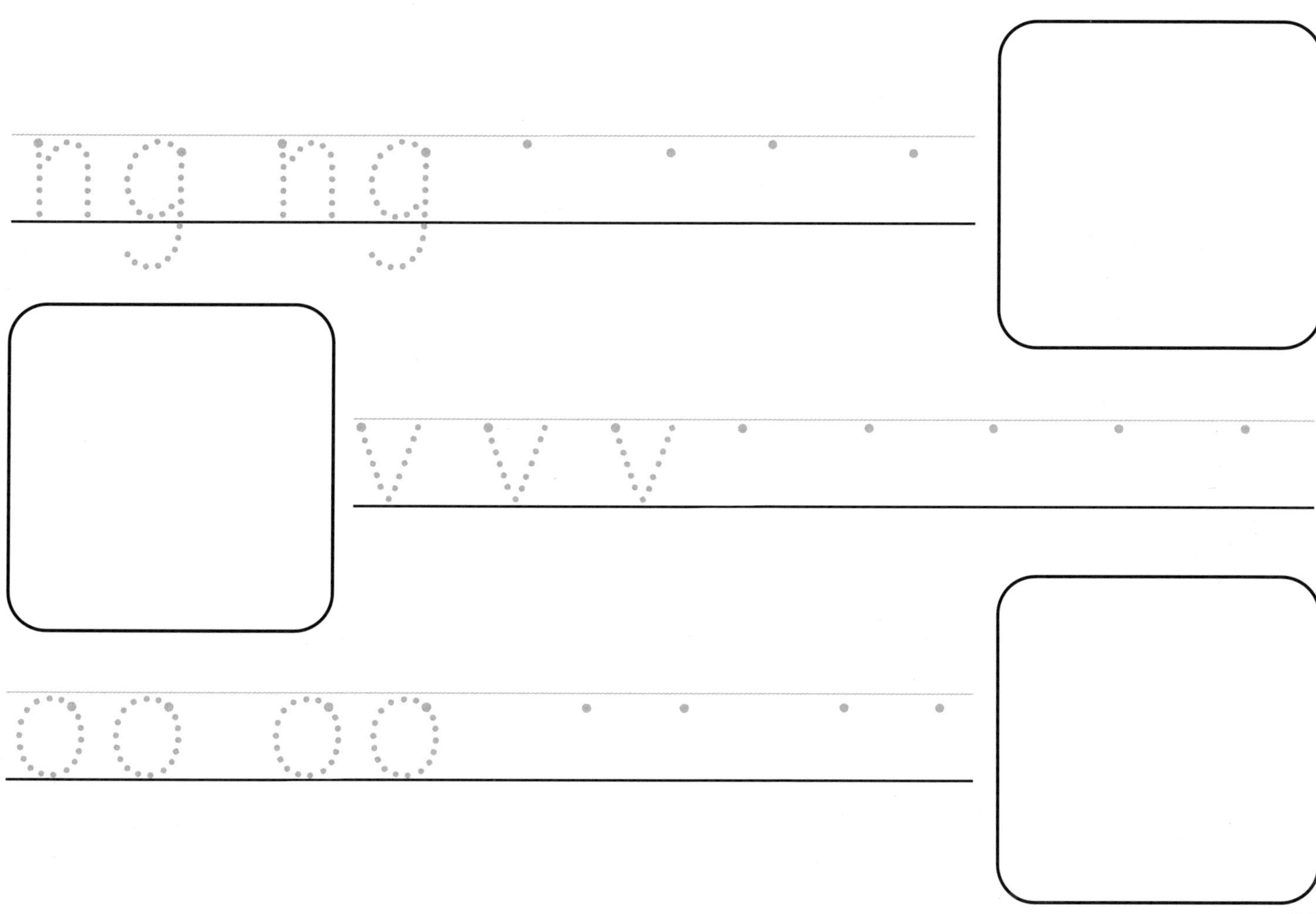

Ages 4+

Jolly Phonics Handwriting Book

Perfect for practicing letter formation

These handwriting books provide letter formation practice for beginner writers. Dotted letters and words (with starting dots) remind students how the letters are formed, and encourage them to write words using the letter sounds they know.
Each page features fun activities to complete and attractive pictures to color, which help the students to develop fine motor control.

This book contains the following letter sounds:

Group 1:	s a t i p n
Group 2:	c k e h r m d
Group 3:	g o u l f b
Group 4:	ai j oa ie ee or
Group 5:	z w ng v oo oo
Group 6:	y x ch sh th th
Group 7:	qu ou oi ue er ar

To see the full range of Jolly Phonics products, visit our website at www.jollylearning.com

MIX
Paper | Supporting responsible forestry
FSC® C016973

82 Winter Sport Lane, Williston, VT 05495, USA. Tel: +1-800-488-2665
77 Hornbeam Road, Buckhurst Hill, Essex, IG9 6JX, UK. Tel: +44 20 8501 0405
Printed in China.

www.jollylearning.com info@jollylearning.co.uk

ISBN 978-1-83582-185-5

Reference: JL1855